52

Sketch Prompts

WEEKLY ART PROMPTS FOR CREATIVE DOODLING & BEYOND

by: Samantha Cole

Published in 2017 by
Samantha Cole
Bazaar Encounters, LLC

ISBN: 978 0 996764193

THIS BOOK IS MEANT FOR ARTIST AND
CREATIVES OF ALL SKILL LEVELS.

IN THIS BOOK YOU WILL FIND 52 WEEKLY SKETCH
PROMPTS TO INSPIRE YOU TO CREATE.

DO NOT BE AFRAID TO BREAK THE RULES OR
TWEAK THE PROMPT IF YOU HAVE A BETTER IDEA.
DO NOT HOLD BACK ON YOUR OWN IDEAS!

THE PROMPTS ARE THERE TO HELP YOU, NOT
RESTRICT YOU.

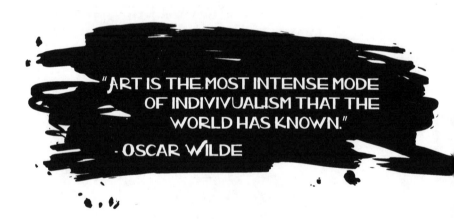

"ART IS THE MOST INTENSE MODE
OF INDIVIVUALISM THAT THE
WORLD HAS KNOWN."
- OSCAR WILDE

IT IS UP TO YOU HOW IN DEPTH YOU WANT TO
TAKE EACH PROJECT. RESEARCH NEW THINGS,
REFERENCE OLD THOUGHTS & REMEMBER
TO THINK OUT OF THE BOX.

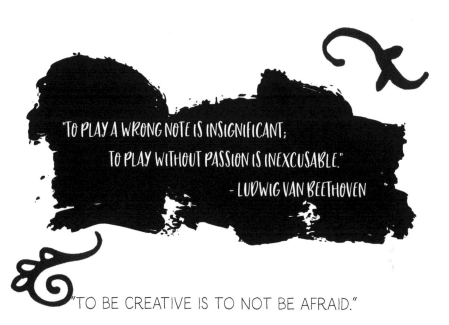

"TO PLAY A WRONG NOTE IS INSIGNIFICANT;
TO PLAY WITHOUT PASSION IS INEXCUSABLE."

- LUDWIG VAN BEETHOVEN

"TO BE CREATIVE IS TO NOT BE AFRAID."

IN THIS BOOK DO NOT BE AFRAID: TO GET MESSY, TO CROSS THE LINE, TO EXPERIMENT, TO EXPRESS YOURSELF TRUTHFULLY, AND MOST IMPORTANTLY DO NOT BE AFRAID TO FAIL. IT IS THE ONLY WAY WE LEARN TO CREATE.

BUT ABOVE ALL ELSE - DO & CREATE WHAT YOU LOVE.

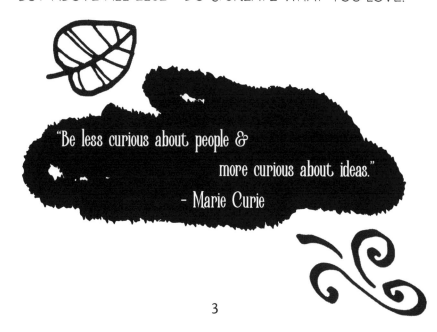

"Be less curious about people &

more curious about ideas."

- Marie Curie

3

Week One: Let's begin with you. Your Fingerprint is uniquely yours. Like snowflakes, no two are alike. Use your fingerprint to design this page. Express yourself with your personal unique marker.

WEEK TWO: FIND AN OLD MAGAZINE AND CUT OUT WORDS FROM TITLES. USE THESE FOUND WORDS TO MAKE A POEM. FILL THE PAGE.

WEEK THREE:
WHAT ARE GROWING IN THESE PLANTERS?

Week Four: Fill these pages with tree rings. Illustrate
between the rings. What did the tree see?
What did it feel? Tell it's story.

WEEK FIVE: GO OUTSIDE AND DRAW A
LIVING THING FROM LIFE. DO QUICK ONE
MINUTE SKETCHES AND GESTURES.

Week Six: Create a pair of wings.

Who or what do they belong to?

WEEK SEVEN: DRAW THE TOP FIVE ITEMS ON YOUR BUCKET LIST.

COME BACK AND DATE THEM AS YOU
COMPLETE EACH ITEM.

WEEK EIGHT:
COLLECT SOME PAINT
SWATCHES AT A
HARDWARE STORE.
COLLAGE THEM.
DOODLE INSIDE THEM.

WHAT WORLDS OR
THINGS EXIST IN
THE INDIVIDUAL
COLORS YOU HAVE
GATHERED?

WEEK NINE: DRAW A PUG OR YOUR
OWN PET IN A VERY SERIOUS
PROFESSION.

Week Ten:

ake an Illuminated Letter.

Do your initials or some of your favorite letters.

WEEK ELEVEN:
MAKE A MAP OF YOUR INNER WORLD.
DRAW YOUR FAVORITE PLACE, YOUR FAMILY,
OR JUST WHAT IS INSIDE YOUR HEAD.

**Week Twelve: Draw what is outside your window.
Did you notice anything new?**

Week Thirteen:
Design a Mask, personalize it to your own passions,
or embellish it with what represents the secret you.

WEEK FOURTEEN: USING A RANDOM CORDIANTS GENERATOR OR A WORLD MAP - LAND YOURSELF IN A RANDOM PLACE IN THE WORLD.

CREATE A LOST OR SUNKEN TREASURE THAT
WOULD BE FOUND IN THAT PLACE.

Week Fifteen: Pick a word that means something to you.
Find images and items to collage on this page that relate or represent that word.

Week Sixteen: Find some music videos with people dancing or videos of animals in motion. Pause and do several quick sketches of interesting poses.

Week Seventeen: Design feathers for birds that do not exist. Give each feather a name.

Week Eighteen: Make your own Periodic Table that includes all the important elements of your life: People, Places, Objects, Animals, etc.

Week Ninteen: Find tape that is not too sticky.
Make a design using different lengths and
cut shapes from the tape.

Color the page between the lines, then remove the tape
and doodle some more!

Week Twenty: Illustrate an alien visitor.
Where did they come from? Did they bring anything?

Week Twenty-One: Time to get a new toothbrush!
Dip the brush tip in white paint and spray the page with speckles.

Make constellations from the new stars you created in this dark sky.

Week Twenty-Two: Write someone a hand written letter.

Decorate the envelope to send your someone Mail Art.

Doodle, paint and have fun! Practice some designs on this page!

Week Twenty-Three:
Design or Redesign your favorite food or drink label.

If making your own: Have fun with the name, make a character for the label. Get some inspiration by looking at what you have at home or at the store.

Week Twenty-Four: Find a dictionary
(book or online) and flip to a random page and point to a
word without looking. Illustrate that word without
writing the word anywhere on this page.

Week Twenty-Five: Sketch your own plant that is also part animal.
Does it produce fruit, veggies, or flowers? Or is it a towering carnivorous tree?
Give it a scientific name and classification, too.

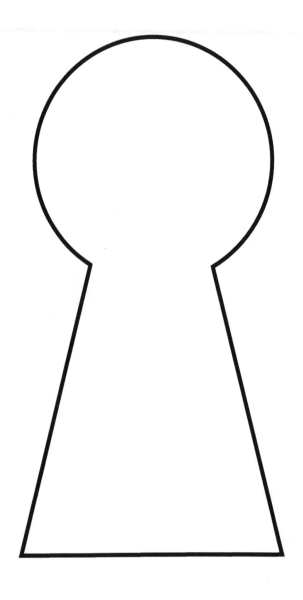

Design the key that opens the door on this page.

Week Twenty-Seven: Start doodling at one corner of this page. Leave no open space!

Week Twenty-Eight: **Create your compass, where is it pointing to? Design the destination on the opposite page.**

Week Twenty-Nine: Design a wand, or staff that you would use to create your own magic.

Week Thirty: Design a set of Nesting Dolls and give them a theme: food chain, skylines based on city sizes, colors of the rainbow, etc.

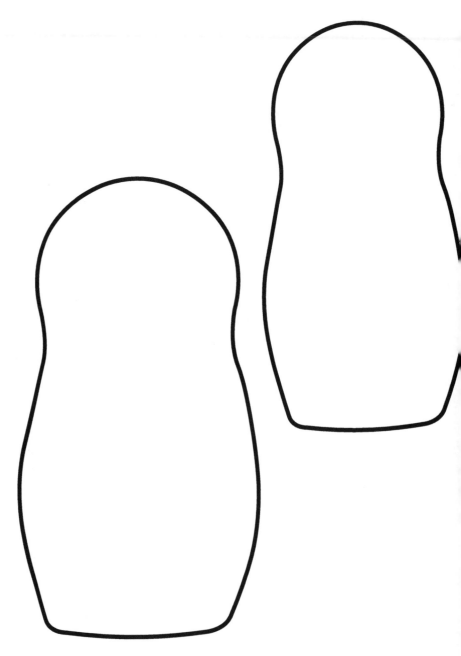

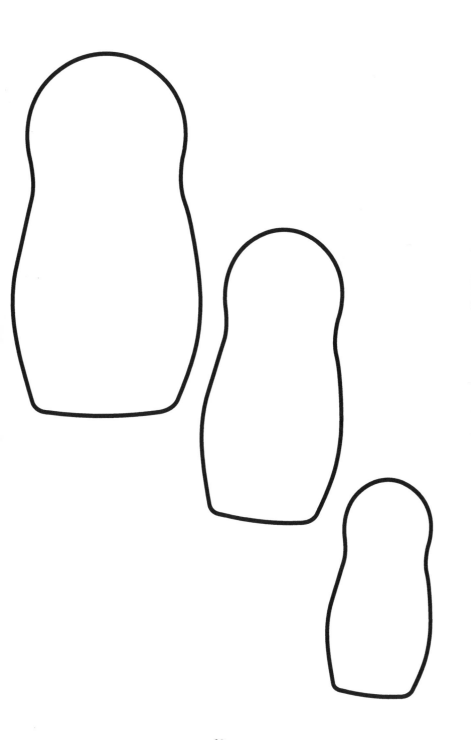

Week Thirty-One: Design a series of stamps illustrating places that you would like to travel to.

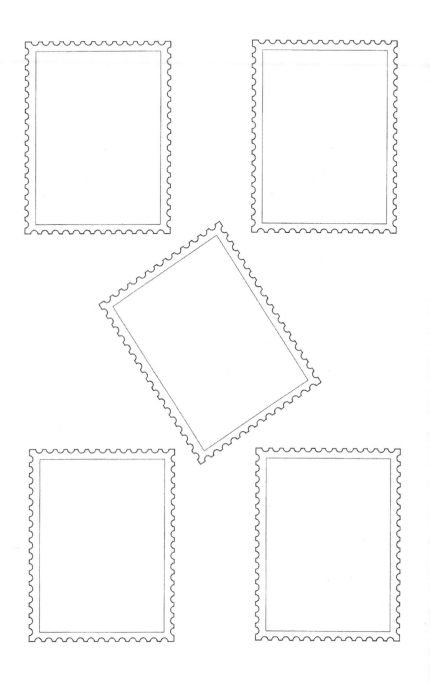

Don't limit yourself. Include destinations also
found in books, different time periods
or deep space.

Week Thirty-Two: Find a flower. Dip the tip of the blossom in paint or ink and make a pattern. Imagine that you are designing a pattern for a textile.

Week Thirty-Three: Design an Emblem or Coat of Arms that describes you or your family. If you know your emblem, modernize it.

Week Thirty-Four: Have you or someone you know ever been **HANGRY**? What do they become in this ferocious state?

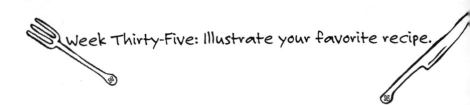

Week Thirty-Five: Illustrate your favorite recipe.

Week Thirty-Six: Put on your favorite song or album. Draw what you think of as you listen - or draw how it makes you feel.

Week Thirty-Seven: Cute Animals in SPACE. What worlds have they conquered. Or are they just spreading joy across the universe?

WEEK THIRTY-NINE: GO TO A CAFE AND
SKETCH WHAT OTHER PEOPLE ORDERED.

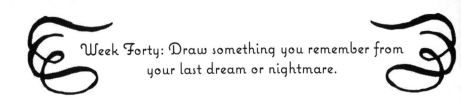

Week Forty: Draw something you remember from
your last dream or nightmare.

Week Forty-One:
Design face cards
for a playing card
deck. Make your
own suits and
characters.

Week Forty-Two: What vehicle would take
you on a grand adventure?
Where are you going?

Week Forty-Three: Find some rocks big enough to paint on. What creatures or animals do you see in them. Paint the creatures on the rocks. Sketch some ideas here.

Week Forty-Four: Drop Ink onto one side of this spread. Close the book for a moment, then open & let dry. What does the ink blot make you think of? Doodle or write what the ink blot makes you think of on top of it.

Week Forty-Five: What does your Yin & Yang look like?
Are your dualities Characters, Animals, Places, or Objects?

Week Forty-Six: Find three different magazines and cut out three pieces of different people, objects and animals from each of them. Collage a crazy scene using the nine elements you have found.

Week Forty-Seven: Now is your chance, invent an ice cream flavor! Put anything you want in it. How would you present this frozen masterpiece?

"Why, sometimes I 've believed as many as six impossible things before breakfast."

Week Forty-Eight: Inspired by this quote from Lewis Carroll, draw your own six impossible things.

Week Forty-Nine: Finish the sentence with an illustration:

"Release the _____."

Week Fifty: Design a fantastic outfit for yourself or your favorite character.

Week Fifty-One: Make an anagram of your name. Illustrate it, or something to go with it.

Anagram is a name with letters rearranged to create a new name or phrase.

Week Fifty-Two: Pick your favorite art style and draw something around you or from your head, in that style.

Made in the USA
Middletown, DE
02 June 2018